The Three Little Pigs
a British folk tale

SCOTT, FORESMAN AND COMPANY • GLENVIEW, ILLINOIS
Dallas, Tex. • Oakland, N.J. • Palo Alto, Cal. • Tucker, Ga. • Brighton, England

ISBN 0-673-10622-5

The Three Little Pigs

Once upon a time there were
three little pigs.
One day the three little pigs left home.
Each little pig wanted to build a house.

The first little pig made a house of straw.

The second little pig made a house of sticks.

The third little pig made a house of bricks.

A big bad wolf saw the little pigs.
"A little pig will make a good
lunch for me," he said.

The big bad wolf went to the house
of the first little pig.

The wolf called, "Little pig, little pig,
let me come in."

"Not by the hair of my chinny chin chin!"
said the first little pig.

"Then I'll huff and I'll puff and I'll
blow your house in!" called the wolf.

So he huffed and he puffed and he
blew the house in.

But the first little pig got away.
He ran into the woods to hide.

The big bad wolf went to the house
of the second little pig.

The wolf called, "Little pig, little pig,
let me come in."

"Not by the hair of my chinny chin chin!"
said the second little pig.

"Then I'll huff and I'll puff and I'll
blow your house in!" called the wolf.

So he huffed and he puffed and he
blew the house in.

But the second little pig got away.
He ran into the woods to hide.

The big bad wolf went to the house
of the third little pig.

The wolf called, "Little pig, little pig,
let me come in."

"Not by the hair of my chinny chin chin!"
said the third little pig.

"Then I'll huff and I'll puff and I'll
blow your house in!" called the wolf.

So he huffed and he puffed, and
he huffed and he puffed.
But the wolf couldn't blow the house in.

The wolf got on top of the house.
He called, "Little pig, little pig!
I'll come down the chimney and
eat you up!"

The third little pig took the cover
off the pot of water.
The water was very hot.
The little pig called, "Come on down!"

The wolf slid down the chimney.
He landed in the water with a big splash.
And that was the end of the big bad wolf.

The Wolves in Our Woods

The wolves in our woods have new pups,
    one, two, three,
A gray one, a white one,
    a black one for me.
The mother and father wolves
    care for their pups.
They feed them and teach them
    and help them grow up.

Houses

These children made some houses.

A girl made a house out of boxes.

A boy made a house out of a box and some candy.

A girl made a house out of blocks.

What could you use to make a house?